Jack and Me and the Ball

Me!

Mick Gowar

Illustrated by Lesley Harker

W

FRANKLIN WATTS

NEW YORK • LONDON • SYDNEY

My brother Jack and me were
playing football in the garden when
the ball went up into the tree
and didn't come down
...as far as we could see.

"It must be stuck," said Jack.
"But I'll get it down – easy!"
And he threw a stick up in the tree.

But the ball didn't come down.
"I've got a good idea," said Jack.
"Your baseball bat – we'll use that!"
And he threw it up into the tree.

But the ball didn't come down.
We tried everything that
Jack could think of –
the garden broom... Mum's umbrella...
Dad's golf clubs...
and a few more things besides.

I'm going to find another tree.

But nothing worked.

"There's only one thing left," said Jack.

"I'll have to climb up into the tree.

Bend down."

"Ow!" I said

"Don't fuss," said Jack.

"Stand in front of the tree!" yelled Jack.

"Get ready to catch!"

"I'm going to shake the tree."

It worked! Down came the garden broom...

Mum's umbrella...

my baseball bat... the stick...

and a few more things besides.

And there behind the tree was...

"Look Jack! The ball!"
"Help!" yelled Jack. "I'm stuck!
I can't get down at all!
     Do something!"

Lots of things have come down. But now who's up the tree?

"Don't worry, Jack!" I cried.
"I know exactly what to do.
I learnt it all from you!
Leave it to me."

And I threw a stick up
in the tree.

Up

Over

Down

Under

Behind

In front

Through

Sharing books with your child

Early Worms are a range of books for you to share with your child. Together you can look at the pictures and talk about the subject or story. Listening, looking and talking are the first vital stages in children's reading development, and lay the early foundation for good reading habits.

Talking about the pictures is the first step in involving children in the pages of a book, especially if the subject or story can be related to their own familiar world. When children can relate the matter in the book to their own experience, this can be used as a starting point for introducing new knowledge, whether it is counting, getting to know colours or finding out how other people live.

Gradually children will develop their listening and concentration skills as well as a sense of what a book is. Soon they will learn how a book works: that you turn the pages from right to left, and read the story from left to right on a double page. They start to realize that the black marks on the page have a meaning and that they relate to the pictures. Once children have grasped these basic essentials they will develop strategies for "decoding" the text such as matching words and pictures, and recognising the rhythm of the language in order to predict what comes next. Soon they will start to take on the role of an independent reader, handling and looking at books even if they can't yet read the words.

Most important of all, children should realize that books are a source of pleasure. This stems from your reading sessions which are times of mutual enjoyment and shared experience. It is then that children find the key to becoming real readers.